28/10/19

D0238293

Please return/renew this item by the
last date shown to avoid a charge.
Books may also be renewed by phone
and Internet. May not be renewed if
required by another reader.
www.libraries.barnet.gov.uk

BARNET
LONDON BOROUGH

First published in Great Britain in 2018 by The Watts Publishing Group

Text copyright: Tony Lee 2018
Illustration copyright © Wil Overton 2018

Illustrator: Wil Overton
Design Manager: Peter Scoulding
Cover Designer: Cathryn Gilbert
Production Manager: Robert Dale
Series Consultant: Paul Register
Executive Editor: Adrian Cole

HB ISBN 978 1 4451 5751 1
PB ISBN 978 1 4451 5752 8
Library ebook ISBN 978 1 4451 5753 5

Printed in China

Franklin Watts
An imprint of
Hachette Children's Group
Part of The Watts Publishing Group
Carmelite House
50 Victoria Embankment
London EC4Y 0DZ

An Hachette UK Company
www.hachette.co.uk

www.franklinwatts.co.uk

AGENT OF P.A.W.S.

TONY LEE AND WIL OVERTON

LONDON·SYDNEY

THE BRITISH MUSEUM.

I'M SO **EXCITED**, DAD! I'VE ALWAYS WANTED TO COME HERE!

I KNOW! WHO WOULD HAVE THOUGHT THAT FILLING OUT A **CROSSWORD** WOULD WIN US A TRIP!

PERHAPS THEY'LL GIVE YOU AN **AWARD**! PERHAPS --

-- ARE **DOGS** ALLOWED IN HERE?

AROOGA! AROOGA! AROOGA!

THIS WASN'T AN ACCIDENT - THEY **DELIBERATELY** TOOK DAD!

I HAVE TO **SAVE HIM** --

-- EVEN IF I HAVE TO **CLIMB IN!**

WHOA!

WHAT ARE YOU DOING?

THEY'LL FIND A WAY TO DO THE RITE WITH OR WITHOUT US —

— AND I HAVE TO ADMIT, I'M **CURIOUS** TO SEE WHAT HAPPENS!

PLEASE — MY DAUGHTER IS OUT THERE ——

SILENCE! IF THE GOOD PROFESSOR WANTS TO READ THIS —

— THEN WE SHOULD **ALLOW HIM TO!**

YES, THE NEWLY DISCOVERED PIECE HELPS **TRANSLATE** IT—

— I CAN SEE HOW THE **RITUAL WORKS!**

DID YOU HEAR THAT? SOUNDS LIKE **DOGS**!

THAT'S **NO DOG** I'VE EVER MET!

WHAT IS EL DOGGO PLANNING?

THE **RITE OF ANUBIS**! HIS HUMAN SOLDIERS WILL BECOME AN **IMMORTAL DOG ARMY**!

THE **QUEEN** OF THE CAT SPIES IS HAPPY TO FILL THE WORLD WITH **IMMORTAL DOGS**?

WELL, WHEN YOU PUT IT LIKE THAT...

YOU CANNOT STOP HIM!

ONLY BY SAYING THE RITUAL **BACKWARDS** CAN IT BE STOPPED!

SO THE **RITE OF ANUBIS** FAILED...

ALL I NEED NOW IS TO TRANSLATE THE **RITE OF BAST,** THE **CAT GODDESS** –

– THEN I CAN TURN EVERYONE INTO CATS!

MINIONS! WE LEAVE NOW!

STOP CHASING THAT **LASER** POINTER!

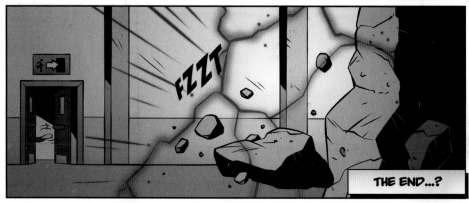

FZZT

THE END...?